FANTASTIC FOUR
RISE OF THE SILVER SURFER
ANNUAL 2008

INSIDE

MARVEL

Fantastic Four: Rise of the Silver Surfer Annual 2008 is published by Panini Publishing, a division of Panini UK Limited. Office of publication: Panini House, Coach and Horses Passage, The Pantiles, Tunbridge Wells, Kent TN2 5UJ. Marvel, The Fantastic Four, Silver Surfer, and all related Marvel characters and the distinctive likeness(es) thereof is/are trademark(s) of Marvel Characters, Inc., and are used with permission. Copyright © 2007 Marvel Characters, Inc. All rights reserved. www.marvel.com Fantastic Four Motion Picture: © 2007 Twentieth Century Fox Film Corporation. All rights reserved. Dodge is a registered trademark of DaimlerChrysler Corporation. No similarity between any of the names, characters, persons and/or institutions in this edition with those of any living or dead person or institution is intended, and any such similarity which may exist is purely coincidental. This publication may not be sold, except by authorised dealers, and is sold subject to the condition that it shall not be sold or distributed with any part of its cover or markings removed, nor in a mutilated condition. This publication is produced under licence from Marvel Characters, Inc. through Panini S.p.A. Printed in Italy.
ISBN: 978-1-84653-050-0

99

ONE OF ROCK. ONE OF FLAME. ONE OF ELASTICITY. ONE OF INVISIBILITY. THEY ARE THE...

FANTASTIC FOUR

REED, SUE, JOHNNY AND BEN. A family united by one fateful trip in an experimental spacecraft – a trip that was supposed to bring scientific glory, but instead brought an intense bombardment of cosmic radiation. This radiation changed those on board the spacecraft in ways they could never imagine, granting them each amazing powers, and the opportunity to become *Mr Fantastic, The Invisible Woman, The Human Torch* and *The Thing* – Earth's first family of Super Heroes, the *Fantastic Four!*

MR. FANTASTIC

Real Name:

Reed Richards

Height:	Weight:
6 feet 1 inch	180 pounds

Powers: *Can stretch, deform or expand his body into any shape he can think of*

Quote: *"If I could just calibrate the quantum deregulator...."*

CELEBRATED around the world as much for his brilliant scientific mind as his stretching abilities, Reed Richards commands the respect of his peers and family as leader of the Fantastic Four.

His mastery of mechanical engineering, chemistry, physics and biology are unsurpassed, and his inventions are vital in the team's ongoing battle against their enemies.

But with his impending marriage to Sue Storm, the ever-present threat of his arch-enemy, Victor von Doom, and a new menace in the shape of one of the galaxy's most powerful heralds, might saving the Earth *and* remembering his wedding vows be too much even for Mr Fantastic's great mind?

POWER UP

As well as being able to stretch his body up to 3 miles, Reed's brilliant mind invented the Fantasticar, which can fly at heights of 30,000 feet and speed along at over 500 mph. Not bad for a family run around!

FANTASTIC FACT

Mr Fantastic's body is so elastic, bullets, missiles and knives bounce right off him!

INVISIBLE WOMAN

Real Name:
Susan Storm

Height:	Weight:
5 feet 6 inches	120 pounds

Powers: *Can turn herself and other people or objects invisible at will; can create invisible force fields and constructs*

Quote: *"Quit arguing you two!"*

ENGAGED to Reed, and older sister to Johnny, Sue Storm is the glue that binds the Fantastic Four together.

She may be the mother of the team, but she's no pushover in battle – as her powers of invisibility develop, so her confidence grows too, and she plays more and more of an active role in the team's leadership.

And it is these powers and leadership skills that will be put to the ultimate test, as her family has to deal with not one, but two beings of immense strength, intelligence and power.

FANTASTIC FACT

The Invisible Woman can make protective force fields that are up to several miles wide!

POWER UP

As if turning herself invisible wasn't cool enough, Sue can also do the same to other objects and people, make massive invisible battering rams, and animate the energy around her to make ramps, slides, and even stairs to allow her to travel through the air.

HUMAN TORCH

Real Name:
Johnny Storm

Height:	Weight:
5 feet 10 inches	170 pounds

Powers: *Can cover his whole body in fire; can shoot fireballs; can manipulate existing flame; can fly at supersonic speeds*

Quote: *"FLAME ON!"*

OFTEN impetuous and immature, Johnny Storm is the youngest, most reckless and most volatile member of the Fantastic Four.

Blessed with what some see as the most destructive powers in the team, this hothead's fiery abilities and temper make him a force to be reckoned with for both friends and foes.

But sometimes this can lead to him rushing into battle without considering the consequences - not a good idea with Doctor Doom and the Silver Surfer around!

FANTASTIC FACT
The Human Torch's white hot Nova Flame can reach 1 million degrees, and destroy a small moon!

POWER UP

Talk about being on fire! Not only does Johnny Storm have the ability to cover his whole body in red hot flames, he can also shoot superheated plasma blasts at enemies. But his biggest weapon? That's his ultra hot Nova Flame!

THE THING

Real Name:

Benjamin Grimm

Height:		Weight:
6 feet		500 pounds

Powers: *Superhuman strength, durability and endurance; above-average reflexes*

Quote: *"IT'S CLOBBERIN' TIME!"*

SINCE *their accidental exposure to cosmic radiation, Ben Grimm has faced the biggest struggle in adapting to his new body.*

This skilled fighter pilot was transformed into a creature with superhuman strength and toughness, but with these powers came a craggy, orange appearance that even a mother would find hard to love!

The only one of the team unable to change back to his human form, Ben faces great social as well as emotional barriers in his new form, but still manages to maintain his sense of honour as well as humour.

FANTASTIC FACT

Because his lungs are bigger than a normal human's, The Thing can hold his breath for 9 minutes!

POWER UP

There's no doubt about it - Ben Grimm's main strength is... well, his strength. He can lift about 85 tons, and his rock-like skin is almost totally impenetrable - he can take just about any hand-fired missile in the chest and still come back for more clobberin'!

FANTASTIC FOUR
STRIP ZONE

GET READY for two of the most fantastic, face-clobberin', flame-filled comic strips you'll ever clap eyes on, as the world's premiere Super-Hero team do battle with not one, but two of the most dangerous villains in the Marvel Universe.

DOOMSDAY!

First up, it's Doctor Doom, one of the Fantastic Four's most powerful and evil foes, who has come to rain on the Fantastic Four's parade. Will he and his Doombots succeed in forcing Mr Fantastic to hand over something that will make Victor von Doom the most powerful being on Earth? Turn the page to find out!

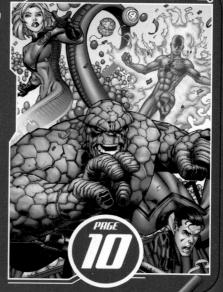

PAGE 10

THE THINGS BELOW

PAGE 38

Then on page 38, see the Fantastic Four confront the first enemy they ever faced as a Super Hero team – the King of Subterranea: The Mole Man! When strange tentacles sprout from deep below the ground to engulf New York City, there can only be one man responsible.... can't there?

FANTASTIC 4
DOOMSDAY!

❹ New York City

One *glimpse* of the *skyline* in the *morning sun* and you'll understand why this is one of the *greatest cities* in the *world*.

But look a bit *deeper,* and you're bound to *discover* that it's those who *dwell here* that make New York *truly--*

--fantastic!

IRRADIATED BY COSMIC RAYS AND TRANSFORMED TO POSSESS SUPERHUMAN POWERS, THEY JOINED TOGETHER TO FIGHT EVIL. **MISTER FANTASTIC**, THE **INVISIBLE WOMAN**, THE **HUMAN TORCH** AND THE **THING**. TOGETHER THEY CALL THEMSELVES THE **FANTASTIC FOUR** IN

DOOMSDAY!

MARC SUMERAK
WRITER

SCOT EATON
PENCILS

JONATHAN GLAPION
INKS

GURUeFX
COLORS

DAVE SHARPE
LETTERS

MICHAEL RYAN and GURU eFX
COVER

JAMES TAVERAS
PRODUCTION

NICOLE WILEY
EDITOR

CADENHEAD and PANICCIA
CONSULTING EDITORS

JOE QUESADA
CHIEF

DAN BUCKLEY
PUBLISHER

Ben Grimm. The Thing.

You *ain't* gonna *get away* with this...

...not *this* time...

Sorry, old friend--

--but this is for your own good!

Johnny Storm. The Human Torch.

Now *this* is why I got into the *super hero biz!*

I thought you said you were *done* with your *new invention,* Reed.

Just working on my *quantum converter.* I want everything to be *perfect* for the *big unveiling.* It's not *every day* that I create a *power source* that could *change* the *world* as we *know* it!

You're *right...* it's every *other* day!

But I think you've run *enough tests* for now. Time to put the *toys* away and *join the fun.*

Right... *fun.*

Don't worry, dear. I'll keep it nice and safe with *Ben's gadget* until you need it.

What's the *matter*, Benjy-boy? Still *mad* that Suzie confiscated your *tunes*?

Nah... it's not *that*.

I just don't feel much like *celebratin'* the fact that I'm a *monster*.

I mean, *you* got yer *cool powers*, yer *fan club*, yer *groupies*...

Well, *hello there*, ladies!

...all *I* get is a *balloon* that makes me look like I'm in *desperate need* of *Weight Watchers!*

Are you *kidding* me? There've gotta be *dozens* of fans out there who'd *love* to get a *smile* from that *ugly mug* o' yours!

Gee... *thanks*...

No prob, pal! Now *cheer up* and give our *adoring public* what they *want!*

Umm, *kid*... I *hate* to *rain* on our *parade*...

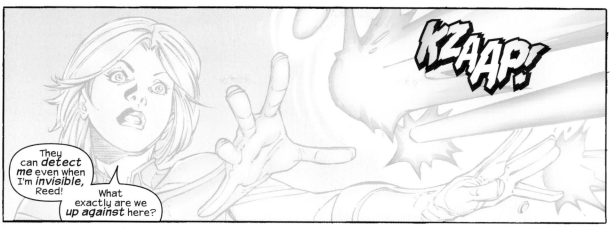

KZAAP!

They can *detect* me even when I'm *invisible*, Reed! What exactly are we *up against* here?

KZAAP!

We'll know in a few--

Oh. Well, that's *just* what I was hoping!

My *scans* have detected *no signs of life.*

Despite their *fancy exteriors*, it seems our *attackers* are nothing more than the *next generation* of Doombot.

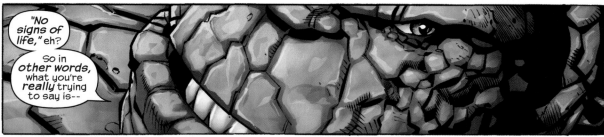

"*No signs of life*," eh?

So in *other words*, what you're *really* trying to say is--

--it's CLOBBERIN' time!

Looks like your *robo-goons* are ready for the *scrap heap*, metal mouth!

And now that *they're* outta the way, you're the *next guest* on *"Extreme Makeover: Thing Edition"*.

That was merely a *fraction* of the *power* that Doom holds.

Even *now*, more of my *android warriors* are ready to *unleash* attacks that will *crush* your *faithful followers* like the *ants* they are!

Unless, of course, you *give* Doom that which he *seeks*...

What is it that you *want*, Victor?

Do you *truly* need to *ask*, Richards?

The *quantum converter* you planned to *debut* at *today's festivities*.

Surrender it *now*...or watch your city *suffer*!

Soon... Those last few *androids* are *molten metal* now...

...but *unfortunately*, it looks like *Doom got away!*

Don't *worry*, Johnny. I'd say we still have *plenty* to *celebrate* today!

How can you *say that*, Reed?

Yeah! You heard what *Doom* wants to *do* with your *power-thingy!*

Then it's a *good thing* he doesn't *have it!*

Huh?

I *remembered* something that Susan *said* during the *parade*--

--so on *Reed's* cue, I gave Doom another...*similar-looking device* that I *happened* to have *on hand!*

...*similar-looking...?*

Oh, man! You gotta be *kidding* me! Oh, that's *priceless!*

*Wait...*I don't *get* it!

If you didn't give Doom the *power source*, what the heck *did* you--

Aw, No...

...*you didn't...*

MR F'S BRAINBUSTERS

1 One character has been blanked out in each of these panels – can you identify who they are?

2 What does the Human Torch take from The Thing?

A) His favourite baseball cap

B) His MP3 player

C) His watch

3 Which member of the F4 was made into the giant inflatable that is blanked out in this picture from the strip?

4 Whose name is missing from the newspaper headline?

A) BEN GRIMM

B) VICTOR VON DOOM

C) REED RICHARDS

5

We've removed the speech bubble in this picture taken from the strip. Can you work out what The Thing is saying?

A) HOW ABOUT A KNUCKLE SANDWICH, DOOMBOT!

B) OH DEAR, IT SEEMS YOUR FACE GOT IN THE WAY OF MY FIST!

C --it's CLOBBERIN' time!

6 How does Mr Fantastic save the public from falling rubble?

A) Calls The Invisible Woman over to stop it with a force field

B) Stretches his hand out and catches it

C) Forms a canopy with his body to catch it

7 What does the boy want The Thing to sign his autograph on?

A) A piece of toilet paper

B) A Fantastic Four comic

C) An old newspaper

8 What has been added to this scene that shouldn't be there?

9 What song was playing on The Thing's MP3 player?

A) White Christmas

B) Hit Me Baby One More Time

C) Sugar Sugar

10 Finally, put these pictures in the same order that they appeared in the story:

ANSWERS ARE ON THE INSIDE BACK COVER

SILVER SURFER

▸ **Real Name:**

Norrin Radd

Height:	Weight:
6 feet 4 inches	225 pounds

Powers: *Can fly; can phase through and alter the appearance of solid matter; can fire energy beams; superhuman strength*

Equipment: *Cosmic-powered surfboard that is linked directly to the Surfer's mind*

ONE of the noblest, yet most tormented entities in the universe, the Silver Surfer is a speeding bullet of pure cosmic power, primed and ready to herald the destruction of Planet Earth.

Born Norrin Radd on the idyllic planet Zenn-La, he was part of an ancient and advanced civilisation which was free from crime, disease, poverty, or want of any kind. This led to the people of Zenn-La losing the will to strive or explore, leaving the inquisitive Norrin restless, and yearning for adventure.

Be careful what you wish for...

This adventure came in the form of the all-powerful, Galactus, a god-like being, intent on devouring Norrin's home planet of Zenn-La. Faced with this destruction, Norrin attempted to strike a deal with Galactus to serve as his herald, and discover new planets for him to consume, in return for sparing his own.

Rise of the Silver Surfer

Galactus agreed to this deal and imbued Norrin Radd with the Power Cosmic, turning him into the Silver Surfer – a silver-skinned, almost indestructible super-being, blessed with incalculable strength, and able to manipulate the universe's cosmic energies at will.

Now he roams the universe, searching for his master's next planet-sized meal, trying in vain to satisfy the world devourer's insatiable hunger. **And it looks like Planet Earth is next on the menu.....**

POWER UP

The Silver Surfer wields the Power Cosmic, which allows him to absorb and channel cosmic energy, giving him all these incredible super powers:

INVULNERABILITY
The amazing forces binding his silvery skin make him invulnerable to almost all physical harm

GRAVITY MANIPULATION
Allows him to fly at near-limitless speeds on his board

HEALING FORCE
Allows him to revitalise the life energy of any living thing

MOLECULE MANIPULATION
Allows him to phase through solid matter and change its shape

TEMPERATURE IMMUNITY
Allows him to survive in incredibly hot or cold conditions, outer space and hyper-space

ENERGY MANIPULATION
Allows him to create energy beams that can destroy whole planets, and gives him almost limitless strength

TIME MANIPULATION
Allows him to witness past or future events at will, and travel through time

GALACTUS

MASTER of the Silver Surfer, Galactus is an entity of vast cosmic power, and one of the most feared beings in the universe.

> He has near god-like power, allowing him to do almost anything that he wishes, and his scientific knowledge is beyond all human understanding.

> This immense power comes at a price for others though – in order to maintain it, Galactus must devour planets that have the potential for supporting life, often leaving nothing but dust and rubble.

> It is said that without Galactus, energy balances would become unstable, and the universe would collapse. **But just try explaining that to the 6.5 billion humans whose planet is next on his hit list!**

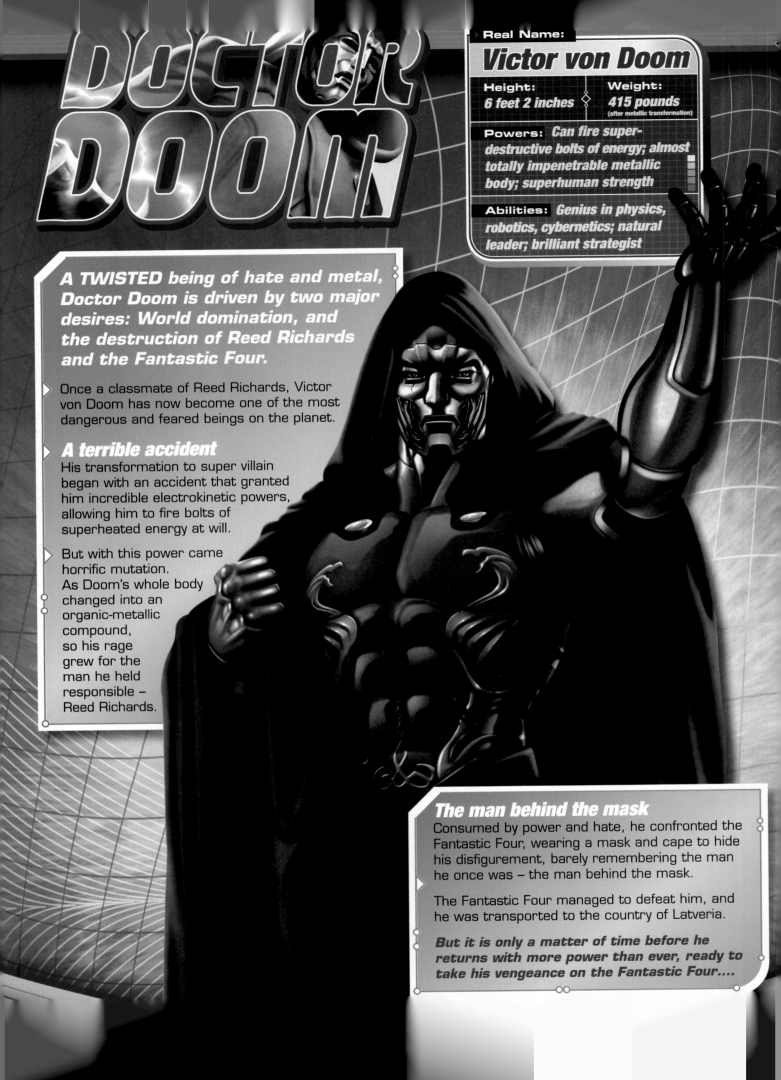

DOCTOR DOOM

Real Name:

Victor von Doom

Height:	Weight:
6 feet 2 inches	415 pounds (after metallic transformation)

Powers: Can fire super-destructive bolts of energy; almost totally impenetrable metallic body; superhuman strength

Abilities: Genius in physics, robotics, cybernetics; natural leader; brilliant strategist

A **TWISTED** being of hate and metal, Doctor Doom is driven by two major desires: World domination, and the destruction of Reed Richards and the Fantastic Four.

Once a classmate of Reed Richards, Victor von Doom has now become one of the most dangerous and feared beings on the planet.

A terrible accident

His transformation to super villain began with an accident that granted him incredible electrokinetic powers, allowing him to fire bolts of superheated energy at will.

But with this power came horrific mutation. As Doom's whole body changed into an organic-metallic compound, so his rage grew for the man he held responsible – Reed Richards.

The man behind the mask

Consumed by power and hate, he confronted the Fantastic Four, wearing a mask and cape to hide his disfigurement, barely remembering the man he once was – the man behind the mask.

The Fantastic Four managed to defeat him, and he was transported to the country of Latveria.

But it is only a matter of time before he returns with more power than ever, ready to take his vengeance on the Fantastic Four....

He may be the Fantastic Four's greatest enemy, but now it's **YOUR** turn to take on Doctor Doom! You'll need to keep your wits about you, as you help the team use each of their super powers to foil his plans for world domination, in our diabolical puzzle mission spread:

DOOMED!

Think you're up to the challenge? Turn the page to find out! ▶▶▶

DOOMED!

DOCTOR DOOM has stolen the quantum converter from the Baxter Building!

Complete all of the challenges to help the team wrestle it back from his evil clutches!

① BREAK IN!

The F4 will have to break into the embassy. Luckily, **The Invisible Woman** can see through the outer casing of the door lock.

Follow each wire from top to bottom, and write the corresponding letter in the boxes below, to spell out the password.

T L I A R V A E

② WITHIN REACH

Now they're inside, **Mr Fantastic** can stretch through the ventilation shafts and grab the convertor.

Only one shaft is short enough for him to reach through - can you tell which one it is?

A
B
C
D

HINT
Use pieces of string to work out which shaft is the shortest.

3 CLOBBERIN' TIME!

Oh no! Mr F has managed to grab the convertor, but it looks like it's triggered the security systems, locking the F4 inside!

Help **The Thing** pick the door with the least amount of resistance to clobber through!

A

Total Resistance
_____ **tons**

B

Total Resistance
_____ **tons**

C

Total Resistance
_____ **tons**

D

Total Resistance
_____ **tons**

KEY:

Blast door
40 tons

Steel door
35 tons

Oak door
5 tons

Steel bars
25 tons

Iron bars
15 tons

Safe lock
10 tons

4 HOT ON YOUR HEELS

Nice work! But now Doom has unleashed his Doombots to track down the F4!

Help the **Human Torch** guide the Fantasticar back to the Baxter building, by finding the route that avoids any Doombots.

FINISH

START

ANSWERS ARE ON THE INSIDE BACK COVER

Fantastic Four

The strange growths have been erupting all over the city for the past hour, coming up through sewer tunnels.

Just in--reports of the tentacles are coming in from all over the Eastern Seaboard. Police and the National Guard are spread thin, trying to combat the new menaces...

Mayor Sharpe. How are the police doing?

They fared better once the National Guard showed up.

I want to thank you and your assistants for help with this.

Assistants?

Happy to help, Mayor.

Can we expect another attack like this? Do you know what these things are?

We don't know, and no.

But we do have a good guess.

"Since these tentacles came from far underground, we have to assume they're connected to the first threat we ever fought together--The Mole Man.

"He was a brilliant outcast who explored the very deepest caverns of the planet years ago. He befriended a race of creatures called Moloids, who accepted him as their leader. With their combined might he built his own kingdom--Subterranea.

"The Mole Man was bitter towards our society for shunning him and his studies. In the past he often tried to take revenge on the surface world. But in recent years, he's been content to exist in his own territory-- an incredibly vast territory.

"Still, it's hard to ignore his talent for controlling bizarre creatures. There's a whole island of giant monsters under his command, and these weird growths seem right down his alley. We're going to investigate him now."

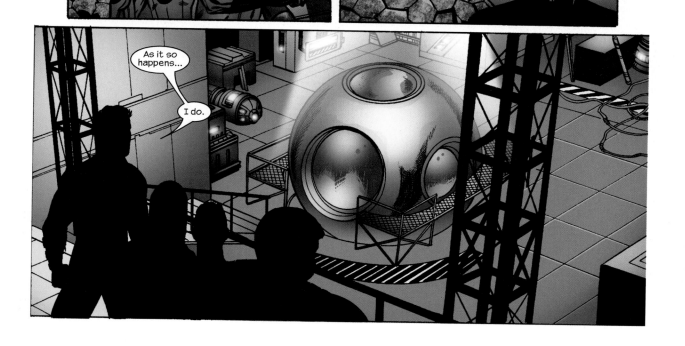

Everyone strapped in?

Yeah, but Ben seems to be in the driver's seat-- *again*.

That's 'cause I'm the pilot of the group, junior.

We're not going through the *air*. Besides, I'm like the big-time stunt-driver!

Guys, this isn't some hot rod to quibble over. Unlike other tunneling machines, this craft doesn't use drills or augers. It generates opposing sonic fields that bust up the rock and expels the rubble to propel us forward.

And it cost as much as a summer action movie with an all A-list cast.

Now Johnny, if you want, you can engage the sonic drive.

Cool!

IWWHHHRRRRRMMMN

WAAAAAHHHHOoOo!

W-what's ha-p-p-peninngg...?!?

We'rrrre about to pass thrrrough the crustttt--to the m-m-mantle!

We'lllll sta-a-a-bilizzze innn aaaa--

--minute.

Ahhh.

Whoa. I can't tell where we're going--it's just a bunch of rocks.

This is why you're not the pilot. See that thing Ben's looking at?

It's the navigation display.

I've charted our course close to paths we've taken before to Subterranea.

And we're detecting slime trails like the ones on the surface nearby, so those tentacles could originate there.

Unfortunately, the sonic drive limits the distance of the navigator's imaging.

So we've got to be prepared for any surprises.

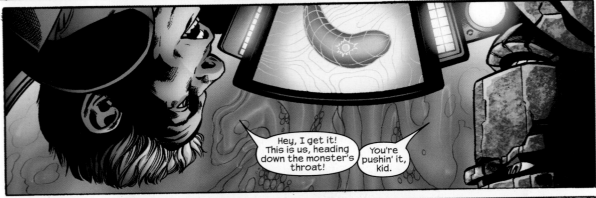

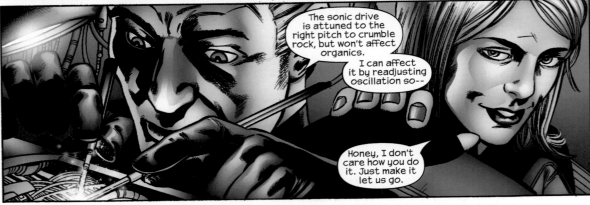

I will not be insulted in my own kingdom.

Leviathus! What have you found?

Hey, put that down!

Do as he says.

GULP

Oh snap.

It's a long walk home. Especially if the creature has grown far enough to reach your world.

Creature?

Ha ha! You think you've been fighting legions! I suggest your most talented member direct her power to that rock wall.

How much rock can you make invisible?

Just watch.

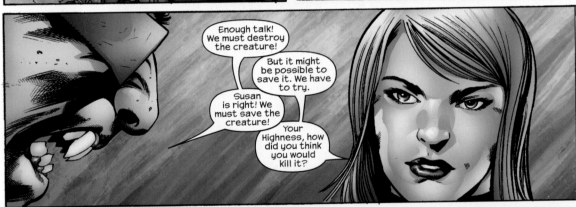

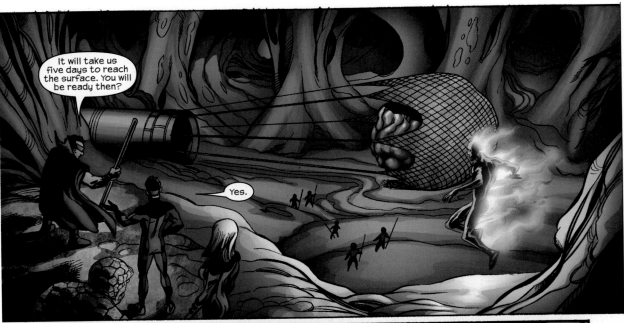

It will take us five days to reach the surface. You will be ready then?

Yes.

"We'll prepare a transport chamber for the nerve center, and Sue's friend, the Mayor, can call her friends in the government...

"...and ask them to donate the largest cargo rocket they have. I'll probably have to modify it to help with the heavy payload."

Once it's in space, we can relocate the animal to a new home, towing it with our own spacecraft.

Speaking of our craft...we need a certain one back to get back above ground.

Anything for the lovely Ms. Storm.

SLURRK

Aw, man... It could have been worse.

That's twice our vehicle has been spit up today!

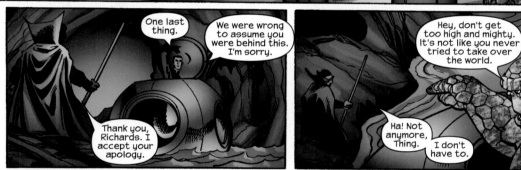

One last thing.

We were wrong to assume you were behind this. I'm sorry.

Thank you, Richards. I accept your apology.

Hey, don't get too high and mighty. It's not like you never tried to take over the world.

Ha! Not anymore, Thing. I don't have to.

Mankind will ruin the surface world one day, and come underground seeking the planet's protection.

Then everyone will have to do things *my way.*

④ The End

MR F'S BRAINBUSTERS

LOOKS like the Mole Man actually helped the Fantastic Four rid Planet Earth of its pest control problem! But how much of their adventure can YOU remember? See how many of these questions you can answer!

1 What was the tentacle crushing in this picture?

2 What was the name of the tentacled beast that was terrorizing Earth?

A) Nickel-Heap **B)** Octo-Beast **C)** Nekal-Gehep

3 Can you spot 5 things that have been changed in this picture from the original strip?

4 We've blanked out what's being said in this picture. Can you work out what the Mole Man is saying?

A — HOW DO YOU DO THAT WITH JUST YOUR HANDS?

B — NOW DO YOU SEE WHAT YOU'RE UP AGAINST?

C — WAIT! IF YOU USE YOUR POWERS WE COULD ALL BE KILLED!

5 One character has been blanked out in each of these panels taken from the story – can you identify who they are?

FANTASTI-QUIZ

NK you've got a brain to match Reed Richards?
kle these perplexing puzzles to find out!

1. Write the answers to the clues in the grid, then rearrange the letters in the red squares to form the bonus word!

BONUS WORD

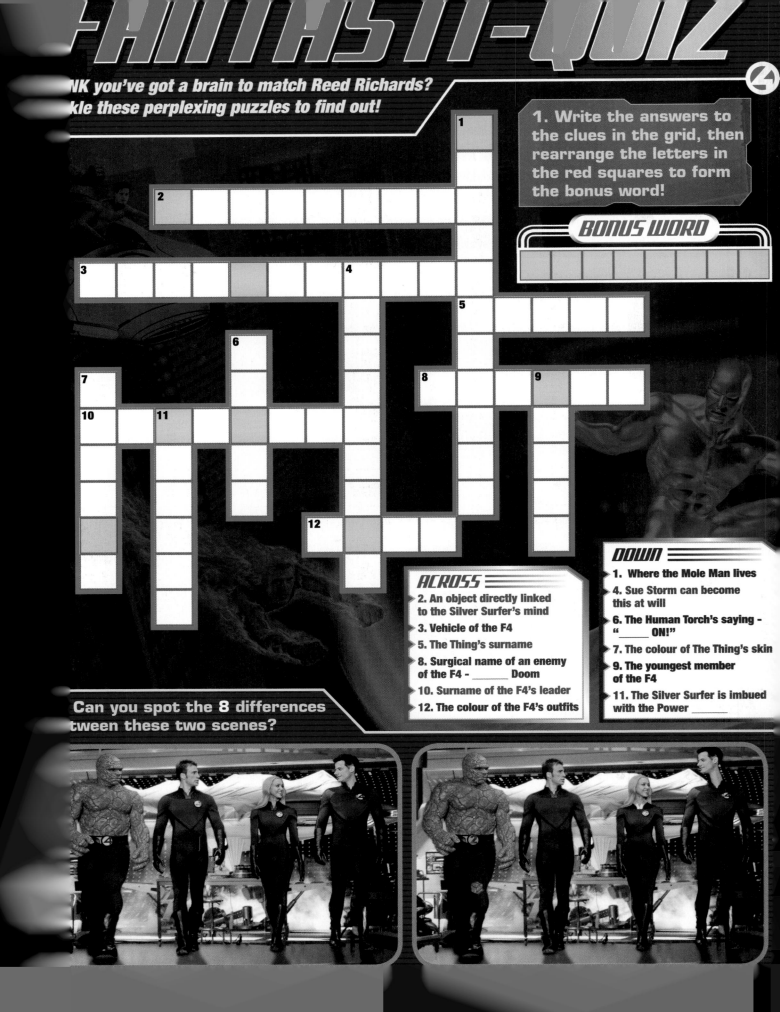

ACROSS

2. An object directly linked to the Silver Surfer's mind

3. Vehicle of the F4

5. The Thing's surname

8. Surgical name of an enemy of the F4 - _____ Doom

10. Surname of the F4's leader

12. The colour of the F4's outfits

DOWN

1. Where the Mole Man lives

4. Sue Storm can become this at will

6. The Human Torch's saying - "_____ ON!"

7. The colour of The Thing's skin

9. The youngest member of the F4

11. The Silver Surfer is imbued with the Power _____

Can you spot the **8** differences tween these two scenes?